23126

Who Goes There In My Garden?

By Ethel Collier. With illustrations by Honoré Guilbeau.
New York: Young Scott Books

It was snowing, it was blowing.
And I had birthday money
from my friend next door.

What fun, to fly down
the cold hill to the store.
What luck, to have money in my pocket.

The store was warm. And on that snowy day,
it was full of garden things.
I could buy a garden!

The old storekeeper told me, "On a snowy day,
it is good to think of gardens.
But wait to plant the seeds.
Wait for the ground to get warm."
So I spent all my birthday money
for beans and flowers.

I said, "My friend next door will help me.
He once had a garden in France."

At home, I put my seeds away and I waited.

Some days it snowed.

Some days there was wind.

Then the rains came
and washed the old snow away.

Now was it time for my garden?
I put my hand on the ground.
I could feel that it was still cold.

Just then my friend from France came out.

"Stop," he said.
"Do not make the garden today.

"I will tell you," he said.
"After the apple tree has flowers,
after all the trees are green,
feel the ground again."

So I waited.

I waited and waited.

And then one day
the apple tree had flowers.

A bird came flying down.
Pick, pick, pick,
and he got a bug from the ground.

"It is time to dig," said the man from France.

I dug up the ground.
When I dug it up, earthworms came out.
Should earthworms go in my garden?

My friend picked up a lump of earth.
He said, "Earthworms eat earth.
They make tunnels down there.
The tunnels let air and water
get under your garden.
Just one earthworm helps.
Ten earthworms help ten times."

Oh, then not one earthworm must get away.

Now, from under the fence,
a toad jumped out.
Should a toad be in my garden?

My friend said, "Toads eat bugs
that eat up gardens.
Far away in France, they have toads to buy,
just to put into gardens."

Oh, then I would keep that toad.

After I had raked the ground,
it was time to plant my beans.
And it was time to plant my flowers.

We found a good stick.
I cut lines with it on the ground.
The lines made beds for the seeds.

I put my seeds in—beans here, flowers there.
And then I covered them.

That was when a ladybug came to my hand.
Oh, ladybug, ladybug, fly away home.
You will eat up my garden.

My friend said, "No! Ladybugs are good bugs.
They eat tiny, tiny bugs that do eat up gardens."

Think of that!

Up on the fence, a spider made a web.
Should I keep the spider too?

The man from France said, "Always keep
the garden spider. Her web catches
enemies of the garden. They fly
into the web. And they stick there
till the spider comes to get them."

Then if all those things help my garden,
that wild brown rabbit must help too.
Does he?

The man from France saw the rabbit.
And he chased it!
"No! No! The garden helps the rabbit.
The rabbit does not help the garden.
A rabbit will eat up your garden!"

But it is my garden, and I like
a wild brown rabbit there.

My first work was done.

My garden was in the ground, waiting.

The sun warmed my seeds.

In the night I could hear
the rain falling on them.

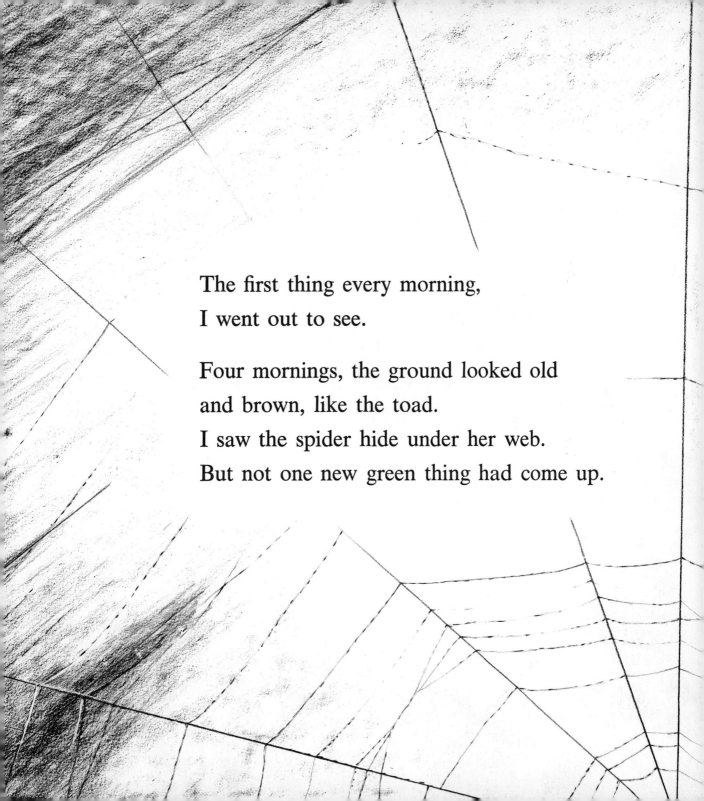

The first thing every morning,
I went out to see.

Four mornings, the ground looked old
and brown, like the toad.
I saw the spider hide under her web.
But not one new green thing had come up.

Then the next morning, I had beans!
Every bean had a round back
and two big hands.
And to get up from the ground,
the beans were doing push-ups.

Soon there were little plants all over,
just where I had put the seeds.
Warm rain and sun came to help them grow.

One bean had the first flower.

But a bee found that flower, and I ran.

"Do not run," said my friend. "The bee
does not look for you. She looks for flowers.
Flowers help the bee make honey."

Summer came. My plants were big.
They covered the ground.
My garden was full of things to pick.

But now I found things that I had never planted.

"Pull out the weeds!" said the man from France.

All summer I pulled weeds.

And I picked flowers and ate beans.

Some days now, the wind blows cold.
The big wild birds are flying over.
This very night, the man from France thinks,
snow will fall.

So I will quickly pick the last of my garden.
Here is a hat full of beans for your dinner.
Here are the last flowers.
You told me who goes in my garden.
Thank you for helping me.